Anyone Can Teach

(they said)

Anyone Can Teach

(they said)

by Rolf E. Aaseng

illustrated by Janna Dory

AUGSBURG PUBLISHING HOUSE

MINNEAPOLIS, MINNESOTA

ANYONE CAN TEACH (THEY SAID)

Library of Congress Catalog Card No. 65-12137

MANUFACTURED IN THE UNITED STATES OF AMERICA

Contents

1. DESPERATE

They must be desperate for Sunday school teachers this year. They even tried to recruit me—without success. Not that I had any good alibis. It's just that the chairman of our congregation's committee on education, who tried to sign me up, didn't seem able to think of any good reasons why I should teach.

First of all she supplied a convenient excuse, in the event it hadn't occurred to me: "I know you're awfully busy . . . ." Who in his right mind would argue about that?

". . . but we can't seem to get anyone to teach Sunday school this year." There's nothing like making a person feel important! What do you suppose she said to the first one on the list? At least she was using good psychology in one respect: so far there had been no chance for me to say no.

"It's asking a lot, I know," she went on, "but

we're wondering if you would do us a favor and consent to teach a class this year." I have nothing against Mrs. Brown, but the appeal to do her a favor didn't arouse any enthusiasm. Maybe my Christian motivation is weak.

"Why me?"

"Well, we have to find someone!"

This second appeal to my ego was not overwhelmingly successful. But thinking it might not be neighborly to say no quite yet, I asked, "What grade did you have in mind?"

"Whatever you prefer. There are still several open."

"You couldn't give me an idea of what the lessons are like," I ventured.

"I'm afraid I haven't looked at them very much," she sighed. "But," she quickly assured me, "they aren't hard. You just follow the book. I'm sure it wouldn't take you much time to prepare; and there's just the one hour on Sunday."

From what I could remember about our Sunday school, it seemed likely that similar advice had been given to most of the teachers.

"I hate to be tied down every Sunday," I objected.

"That's only natural," she agreed pleasantly. "But if you have something really important to do, I'm sure you wouldn't be expected to be present."

"When does the term begin?"

"Tomorrow. That's why I wanted to be sure to see you today."

The interview was getting more painful with every question. So I simply said, "Thanks for thinking of me. But I can't do it."

"But someone has to teach!" she cried in dismay.

"Why?" I asked.

Her mouth popped open—like a goldfish—but no sound came out. A rather perplexed look spread over her face and she slowly walked away.

They're still desperate for teachers.

2. AN E-FLAT CHALLENGE

After all that, I ended up teaching Sunday school!

The pastor called after the committee chairman had left, sold me on the challenge of teaching, and signed me up for a month's trial.

Considering the events of the first Sunday, it's a good thing he emphasized the *challenge* of teaching. That's putting it mildly! Even my nose was challenged—from the moment I opened the door to the "church parlors." Calling a basement the "parlors" doesn't make it smell any better.

The meeting place for the class I was to teach —it wasn't a room, just a corner of the large assembly hall—presented the next challenge. The words of the old song, "Brighten the Corner," state it pretty well. A light bulb or a good lamp would be helpful in meeting this challenge.

At least the chairs are of good quality; they have

to be to last 40 years. I can still remember how big they used to seem when I was perched on top of them, legs dangling, while attending this same Sunday school years ago.

A totally unexpected challenge came that first Sunday when we began to sing. The superintendent announced "Beautiful Savior." The pianist gave a starting chord, which did sound somewhat unusual, and away we went!

I thought I could carry a tune, but this one kept slipping out of my grasp. It sounded as if the piano were falling into a hold every few notes. Everyone seemed to be having the same difficulty—everyone but the pianist, that is. The second stanza was no

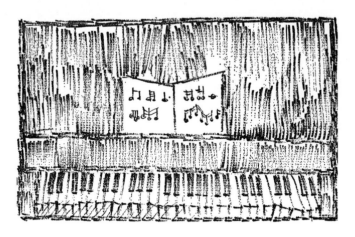

improvement, and by the end of the third, most of us had retired in confusion.

A second hymn seemed to go fairly well, so I concluded that my singing wasn't what it used to be and forgot about it.

But at the end of the period, as we sang "I love to tell the story," I again found myself crowded out on a harmonic limb.

Afterward I decided to ask the superintendent about it. "I thought there was something funny about it too," he said. "Let's ask Margaret."

"Hey, Margaret!" he called to the pianist, who was just leaving. "Has anyone tampered with the piano?"

"Not that I know of. It works about the same as it did last spring."

"Then what made the songs sound so queer to-day?" I asked.

"I don't know," she replied. "Oh—unless it could be that the E flat key doesn't work. I have to play E-natural whenever it is supposed to be E-flat."

She proceeded to demonstrate with "Beautiful Savior."

"Stop!" I hollered. "Get that piano fixed," I shouted to the superintendent. And carried away by the challenge of it, I added, "if I have to pay for it myself."

I did.

3. SOMEONE'S IN THE KITCHEN

"You think your class area is bad!" One of the primary department teachers was reacting to my impressions of my first Sunday.

"Your class meets in the kitchen, doesn't it, Mrs. Gordon," I replied.

"You're telling me!"

"At least it's handy when someone wants a drink."

"Too handy," she snorted. "The kids can't help seeing the faucet, and of course it reminds them that they're thirsty. And while I'm getting Jean a drink, Mark is shinnying up the cupboards to get a glass. It's a rare day when we don't break a glass or a dish."

"Wait till you come to the story of Moses breaking the two tablets of stone while standing on a mountain!" I exclaimed. "Think of the raw materials you have for dramatization."

"It's raw, all right," was her reply. "We sure could have dramatized Jeremiah the day Milton found the sack of onions."

"Surely there must be something good you can say about the room. Isn't it large enough?"

"Yes. And the light isn't bad either. But the temperature leaves something to be desired at times."

"Can't you turn on the stoves if it gets cold?"

"We could, but it creates hazards. We discovered that our hottest day was caused by someone turning on the stove without being noticed."

"At least you have a separate room for your class," I said, still not quite convinced that she didn't have a better deal than I did.

"Most of the time I'd gladly trade it for tables and chairs that fit the children. Even in the kitchen the floor is not the best for sitting on; and the counters are too high."

I was unable to think of any more advantages.

"The main problem, though," she went on, "is all the distractions, and the obviously temporary arrangement. A kitchen was never intended to be a classroom, and the children know they're really out of place there. I never realized the room meant so much."

Mrs. Swenson, who had been standing silently nearby, finally spoke up. "You think you've got it bad. How'd you like to trade classrooms for next Sunday?"

"Where do you teach?" I asked.

"In the women's restroom," was her reply.

4. FOR SOME OF YOU NEWER TEACHERS

"The period just isn't long enough. Why, I never get around to doing the usual things, let alone having time to attempt any of those new ideas they've been trying to teach us."

Mrs. Johnson had cornered me after the teachers' meeting. She was attempting to neutralize the effects of the meeting by telling someone why what we had learned wouldn't work. Then convinced —or at least bolstered—by her own arguments, she could go on in her same old way without being bothered quite so much by her conscience.

"We probably never will have enough time to do what should be done," was my reply. "I'm grateful for these meetings, though. At least they help us to use the time we do have a little better."

"Well, maybe for some of you newer teachers. But as far as I'm concerned, I just can't squeeze another thing into the period."

This conversation began to make me curious. Just how did Mrs. Johnson use her class time? As a result my own class suffered the next Sunday as I tried to overhear what was going on over in her circle.

The worship period was well under way when Mrs. Johnson came huffing and puffing into the room and crowded into a seat. When we dispersed to our classes, she disappeared—maybe to finish dressing, or to put back some hair that was misplaced during the rush—and probably also to rummage around in the supply shelves for something she wanted to use during the class period.

By the time she reached her class they had several lively discussions under way. Naturally they were in no hurry to stop. But she managed to get their attention and called the roll—all eleven names. Each person was asked, "Were you in church last Sunday?" And each one had to call a conference to decide whether he had been there or not. The three absentees became the center of some lively speculation as to their whereabouts.

When she had completed this ritual, Mrs. Johnson took time out to remove her coat and sort out her lesson materials. This gave the class another chance to take off on their own; and they soon came up with a request for a class party.

It caught Mrs. Johnson off guard, and someone suggested that they have a class meeting to decide.

But the president wasn't there, and it took some time to decide who the vice-president was. The discussion got nowhere until one of the girls finally said, "Why don't the officers meet with you and suggest a date to us next Sunday?" This was agreeable to all.

Now to the lesson. "How many have read the chapter?" Mrs. Johnson asked. One hand.

"Well, we'd better read it then."

So one paragraph at a time, the lesson was read aloud by various class members. That's using the term loosely; at best only the reader and the teacher were conscious of what was being read.

There was a slight interruption when the Sunday school secretary came for the reports and Mrs. Johnson had to make something clear to her.

Finally they got to the end of the chapter and were about to start on the questions. Then the dismissal bell rang. As the students were noisily getting ready to leave, Mrs. Johnson attempted to give an assignment.

As she was leaving, she sighed to me, "We just barely got started again today."

5. TRAINED? RATS!

Any move to make Sunday school Christmas programs something for historians to read about in congregational archives has my instant and enthusiastic support. The first such program that involved me as a teacher was more than enough to last a lifetime.

We went at it in the conventional manner: Each class was assigned a section of the program consisting of a sequence of short recitations. In case the recitations weren't audible, each class worked out some sort of visual presentation as well so the program wouldn't be a total waste of time.

The theme of the program was very appropriate, calling attention to Jesus, the Light of the world.

The first part of the program progressed beautifully. The classes who presented it made use of such prophecies as Balaam's prediction in Numbers 24: 17, and the promises of light in Isaiah, and then called attention to the need of the world for this kind of light.

Our part in the program came next. We had taken some class time—actually it amounted to two entire periods—to train for the event, going over individual recitations. Therefore I was fairly sure we wouldn't have any difficulty with that. And the visual device we were going to use seemed so simple that I didn't think we needed much practice on it.

It really wasn't intentional that I missed the final rehearsal on Saturday afternoon. I just got so busy at work that I forgot all about it. No one said anything to me about it, so I assumed everything had gone all right. Later I learned that there had been only a couple of teachers on hand for that rehearsal. Maybe in all the confusion they couldn't tell whether things were going right or not.

At any rate, the program had gone very nicely up to our part. The climax was to follow our class presentation. But it's doubtful that anyone who was there remembers how the program ended.

Our assignment was to tell about the star which guided the Wise Men to the Christ Child, and then to go on to indicate how Jesus, the bright and morning Star, came to bring all nations to God. To call attention to this, we had made large cardboard letters to spell out the word "star." The class members held these in front of themselves as they stood in the front of the church.

You guessed it. With great dignity they marched to the front and displayed their letters—in reverse order!

RATS!

6. ONE FOR THE MONEY

My banker was complaining the other day.

"Children don't have any appreciation of the value of money any more," he grumbled. I was about to add, "Neither does my wife," but he was already elaborating on his theme.

"Why, when I was a youngster, I was plenty grateful to get a penny now and then. And to be handed a nickel called for a celebration! But now—they're insulted if you offer them anything less than a dime or a quarter!"

It's reassuring to have this kind of man for a banker. But to help keep him humble, I said, "If you see any kids with some old pennies they're going to throw away, I'd be grateful if you could persuade them to do it in my back yard."

"They do practically throw them away," he protested.

My mind began to project pictures of children

throwing pennies away—out the window, down the sewer grating, into the street. To my mild surprise, these didn't make strange scenes at all. In fact, I could almost hear the pennies dropping on the floor and rolling into inaccessible corners. This had a familiar ring to it. It led me to observe, "I know one place where kids—and probably grownups, too—think pennies are worth something."

"Where is that?" he demanded.

"Sunday school."

His grunt did not indicate whether he was happy to find this bastion against inflation or not.

Most of the children in my class bring pennies for their Sunday school offering. Yet they accept it as only right that they should have a quarter or more to spend each week on candy and comic books.

The lowly penny has accomplished a great deal in Sunday schools, and in the church generally. But we may have overemphasized the might of the widow's mite.

There is something alarming about the gusto with which we can sing, "If you cannot give your thousands, you can give the widow's mite." It sounds as though we were overjoyed to find justification for our small gifts. It may be a good thing that new hymnbooks seem to be omitting that entire stanza from the hymn.

If "the least you do for Jesus will be precious in his sight," how much more will be the most we can do? I, for one, consider a five dollar bill a great deal more precious than a penny.

7. RIDDLED READING

There must be something edifying about responsive reading as a part of a worship period—it's been done in Sunday schools as long as anyone can remember. Whatever it is, its value seems to elude me.

Take last Sunday, for example. First there was that awkward pause after the page number had been announced. The superintendent waited until the last person found the right page. By that time, of course, most of the audience was looking around or whispering and wasn't prepared to begin reading. However, if he had begun reading sooner, some would still have been rustling pages looking for the passage, and at least a few would just have given up and closed the book.

Our superintendent has the rare foresight to read through the selection ahead of time and thus usually avoids passages that include tongue-twisters such as "Abimelech" or "Ephphatha." Even so, last Sunday the younger participants had trouble with "iniquities" and "transgressions" (don't we all). And we hadn't read many verses before someone began putting a "--st" where a "--th" should have been, and vice versa. Sometimes kids almost lose their bubble gum trying to tack a "--dst" ending on a word. However, since most Sunday school regulars are somewhat accustomed to biblical language, this in itself may not be too distracting.

But in spite of colons and bold face type, eventually someone blurts out a word where he shouldn't. It may have been due to a speck on his glasses or on the page of the hymnal, but Sunday it was the superintendent who omitted a pause and collided with the first row of readers.

And in the next verse, Susie and Johnny enthusiastically bellowed, "Be not like a horse . . ." a whole line before they should have come in. This did not add to the dignity of the service for the boys who were anticipating just such errors—nor for the rest of us.

And the expression with which we read! Turning over the motor in a stalled car produces more expression than we used in saying, "Be glad in the Lord." It sounded like a battery of untuned fog horns just about out of ear shot.

This really wasn't a hearing of the Word of God. It was rather a type of dull game in which we throw meaningless words back and forth. And whoever misses one is out.

8. NAME THAT TUNE

A few Sundays ago some of the high school students came into the Sunday school assembly room several minutes late. Nothing unusual about that, of course. People always come late to Sunday school.

But as they bumbled about looking for places to sit, it seemed to me that these same individuals came in late quite often, usually as a group.

The next Sunday I looked around before entering the building. There they were. Most of the previous Sunday's stragglers were already on hand, way ahead of time, and were talking together outside the church. Yet they waited to enter the building until the opening worship was well under way.

The following Sunday they again were clustered around the entrance. So I asked them, "How come you guys wait until Sunday school has started before you come in?"

"Why not?" replied one. "We don't miss anything. After ten years we should have learned the words for a couple of songs."

I was all set to deliver a sermon on the meaning of worship, gleaned from the last issue of our teachers' magazine. Then I remembered something from a book on making friends and instead asked, "What do you mean?"

"Look, Mac," said one. "We've gone to this Sunday school quite a number of years. Right?"

"Right," I echoed. No one I knew ever had begun coming to Sunday school when he was in high school.

"During this time we have observed that Sunday school begins in the identical same way every Sunday. Right?"

I had never thought of it, so wasn't prepared to verify this statement. But it wasn't necessary. The rest of the group chimed in.

"Yeah: 'Let's all turn to hymn number 33 and sing all verses.'"

"Or: 'We'll begin today with "What a friend we have in Jesus." You all know that, so see how well you can sing it.'"

"Or sometimes it's: 'Jesus loves me.' 'No one needs to look in the book for that!'"

"We figure we've learned those songs well enough," the first speaker concluded.

"So?" I queried.

"So we stand out here and all of us guess what the opening hymn is going to be. If nobody hits it, we go in right away. If we guess right, we come in on the last stanza."

My observations indicated that they didn't miss very often.

Just then the pianist began the introduction for the opening hymn. "You're right again, Tom. That's 'Holy, Holy, Holy.' "

The next Sunday I decided to try their little game—from my usual seat in the assembly room. Sure enough, we sang the very song I guessed.

9. OUT OF SIGHT

"If only we'd known this last Christmas," moaned Bill. The two of us had been pressed into service by the women of the congregation to hunt up last year's banquet decorations. In our search we had finally ended up in the furnace room. And what to our wandering eyes should appear but a well-built manger—much nicer than the one my companion had hastily but laboriously put together the day before the last Christmas program.

"I'd settle for having known it on New Year's Day," I answered. (It still hurts to be reminded of Christmas programs.) "Then at least we wouldn't have had to lug the monstrosity you made up to the storeroom in the bell tower."

"Now we'll have to haul that one down again and throw it away," he added sadly.

"Not so fast! What if this one gets lost again —and you are called on to produce another instant manger?"

This evoked a dismal grunt.

"I should think stuff like this could all be kept in one room," Bill reasoned.

"Maybe. Wonder how much other stuff is stored away here and in other crannies—out of sight and out of mind?"

We decided to find out. A more thorough search of the furnace environs uncovered a slightly damaged blackboard (from the days before they called them chalkboards), as well as a couple of well-damaged chairs, a kerosene lamp, and the fixings for a bazaar fishpond. Upon seeing the last item, Bill commented, "It's just as well that some things get lost. Let's not find this."

We explored other parts of the building. Some fine pieces of lumber were under the stairway to the basement. Bill found some shelves under the back of the altar. "We could have gotten along without buying any Christmas tree decorations if we had known about this," he pointed out when we discovered what was stored there.

"Do we dare look in the kitchen?" I asked.

"I think the women have gone," he said.

So we snooped around. On a top shelf, behind some spare light bulbs (two of which were burned out) and a roll of faded pink crepe paper, we found a stack of unused vacation church school material.

"This could have been returned for credit at one time," I observed.

After we had dug some old paper bags and used candles from a bottom cupboard, we found several nests of teachers' magazines and Sunday school papers. Some were still in their mailing wrappers.

"I'm sure there must be a lesson in this," my friend punned.

"That our wives have something in their spring housecleaning obsession?"

"Or maybe that we need someone to take care of our belongings."

We never did find the banquet decorations.

10. I DREAMT I DWELT IN MURKY HALLS

It seemed that my children came home from school one day and announced that they had been requested to bring money to their teacher every week to pay for their books and supplies.

"How strange," I thought. "That practice was discontinued when I was in grade school. Now public schools provide everything that is needed. Don't tell me that education has progressed to where we were a generation ago."

"Well, maybe it would be worth while to have some of your school books to keep," I commented to the children. But no, they informed me that the books would remain in school for use by other classes next year.

We said no more. The children brought their money every week, and it seemed to be working out all right.

Some time later they invited me to visit school,

and I was happy for the opportunity. (That made me pretty sure it was a dream.) But what a shock! One child met with his class in the boiler room. Another went to the gymnasium where about ten separate classes were seated in circles, a few feet apart.

I sat down at the rear of one of the class circles. The students had no desks, only chairs, and in some classes, tables. The teacher soon came along. She was still wearing her hat and coat, and she kept them on. Picking up a book from the table, she asked her pupils, "Now where were we?" As the period wore on, it became apparent that almost any student, by referring to his textbook (which he had open in front of him), could have done the "teaching."

I stormed out of class to protest to the principal. But I had to wait until the period was over because he was substituting for another teacher who had unexpectedly failed to show up.

When he came to his office, he sympathized with my complaints and acknowledged that the teaching wasn't the best. "But we have to take whom we can get for teachers. If we insist on higher standards or additional training, they may quit. And teachers are hard to get."

"But can't you at least provide teaching helps:

desks, art materials, movies, or something?" I demanded.

"The children haven't brought enough money. Maybe next year or the year after we'll have enough to get some of those things. You see, we are trying to keep the school largely self-supporting."

"That's ridiculous!" I shouted. "My children don't have to pay for their own education. I'll take care of that. Get some qualified teachers; raise salaries or do something! And provide them with equipment. What good is an economical school if it can't teach anything? What I'm concerned about is that my kids learn something, and I'm ready to pay higher taxes . . . ."

That drastic statement woke me up and I found myself sitting in the church basement, alone. Obviously it had just been a nightmare.

11. SUMMER SIESTA

One Sunday morning in July, several of us were standing outside the church enjoying the cool breeze before going in for services. A lady emerged from a car bearing an out-of-state license plate and walked over to us with three kids in tow.

"Pardon me," she said pleasantly. "Could you tell me when Sunday school is?"

"Oh, we don't have any," I replied quickly. It immediately occurred to me that such an answer probably sounded sort of heathenish, so I added, "that is, not at this time of year."

"Why not? What's wrong with this time of year?"

I looked at her with some surprise. She wouldn't even be here as a tourist if it weren't summer. "Well —it's summer."

This didn't satisfy her. "What does that have to do with Sunday school?"

"Why, we never have Sunday school in the summer. That's vacation time."

Now it was her turn to be surprised. "I never heard of such a thing," she gasped. "Don't any of the churches around here have Sunday school during the summer?"

"Oh, sure. The Baptists and Free Methodists do, I think." I was glad for a chance to win at least a measure of approval from this gentle inquisitor. But then it suddenly occurred to me that this made our church look worse than ever. Should I encourage her to skip Sunday school this time—or attend some other church in town? The choice was not a comfortable one.

Maybe she read my mind, because she said, "But yours is the church we would most naturally attend." She mentioned her own denomination; I remembered having heard that church body criticized as being too worldly.

"Do you run your Sunday school all year?" I asked.

"Of course. We think our people need to study God's Word as much in the summer time as in any other season—if not more. And actually they have more time for it."

"Well," she concluded, "if you don't have Sunday school, we can't very well attend it. But I do think it's a very peculiar custom."

12. THE LORD BLESS YOU

While on a vacation trip, our family ended up one Sunday in a town that had no church of our denomination. As we were looking for a worship service to attend, we came upon a Sunday school just about to get under way. Might as well find out how the other half lives, I thought, so we went in.

Before the door had closed behind us, a man who seemed to be purposely stationed near the entrance came over to greet us. "The Lord bless you," were his first words as he extended his hand.

What are we getting into, I wondered. But as it became apparent that he really meant what he said in that greeting, it began to seem appropriate after all.

When I introduced myself as a Sunday school teacher in my home church, he gave me a choice of attending an adult class or visiting the department in which I teach. I decided on the latter, so he introduced me to the teacher. I sat with the class during their opening worship, then went with them to their classroom.

The hymns were different, and the lesson material too; but the schedule and facilities were familiar. However, there seemed to be more enthusiasm and friendliness. It was hard to imagine that these folks had to have their arms twisted before they consented to be teachers. Maybe they even attended teachers' meetings! They didn't stand around the edges during opening exercises, but took part in all of the songs, prayers, and Bible reading, following along in their own Bibles.

What stands out more than anything else from that experience is something the teacher said after class. It explained some of his procedures. With real excitement he told me, "One of my boys gave his heart to the Lord last week. Now there are only two in the class that I'm not sure about. But we're praying, and depending on the Lord to bring them through to faith. There is nothing like the thrill of bringing one of your own class members to the Lord, is there? That's what makes Sunday school teaching so exciting for me."

I was relieved that he didn't ask for the box score in my class. I've taken my class pretty much for granted as far as their faith is concerned. Of course, I think and worry about them: Do they come regularly—do they know their lessons—have they qualified for an award—can they sit through the period without making too much noise?

But that isn't what concerned or excited the teacher I met; and it doesn't give me much of a thrill either. Maybe Sunday school could be more exciting for all of us if I were really concerned about the destination of my students.

It might not even hurt to ask the Lord's blessing on them.

13. ANYONE CAN TEACH

"No thanks, I don't plan to go." Morris was declining my offer of a ride to a church school teachers' institute being held in a neighboring town.

"Why not?"

"It's not worth taking all that time to go down there and sit through a bunch of meetings," he snorted. "They're always trying to make church school teaching look like such a difficult job. You don't have to go to an institute to be a Sunday school teacher. Anyone can teach Sunday school." Apparently he shared the point of view of the chairman of our education committee.

"The fact that you and I are doing it certainly proves that," I said laughing.

He pretended not to hear. "But after teaching —or trying to teach—for a year," I continued, "I'm somewhat interested in finding out how it's done."

"The way you do it really isn't so important," he countered.

"No?"

"Of course not. After all, who does the teaching, you or the Holy Spirit?"

It was obviously a trap, but I gave the proper answer: "The Holy Spirit. But I didn't think the institute was being held for his benefit."

Again Morris seemed hard of hearing. "As long as you give them the Word, so the Spirit can work through it, it doesn't make any difference how you teach or what methods you use."

"If that's the case," I mused, "why don't we play recordings of Bible readings over a public address system? Then we could do away with teachers altogether and not worry about any of us fouling it up."

Morris thought about it a moment. "I don't know. If you could get the kids to listen, it might work. The Word is like seed, you know. All we have to do is plant it."

"Just like in your lawn?"

"Exactly."

"In other words, as long as you use good seed it doesn't make any difference how you plant it. You could lay the seed on top of the ground, or five inches below the surface. Or you could water it every other week with a high pressure stream of water."

"Don't be ridiculous! That's entirely different from teaching Sunday school. Anyway, just going to an institute won't make you a teacher."

"Not any more than attending a flying school will guarantee that you will be a good pilot," I agreed.

"Right."

"But if you don't mind, I'd just as soon that the man who pilots my plane has taken a few lessons, whether they are guaranteed or not."

"It isn't the same situation," Morris objected, showing some irritation.

"No, I don't suppose so. After all, if the plane crashes, you can't lose more than your life. But in Sunday school . . ."

44

14. FIRST SUNDAY AFTER INSTITUTE

"Now things will be different." I was full of confidence as I set out for Sunday school the week after the teachers' institute.

Maybe I should be grateful for small favors and be glad that things were not different—that the hour was still the same cheerful hubbub, rather than a full-sized riot. To say the least, it was difficult to detect any change for the better. Apparently the members of my class hadn't gotten the word that their teacher had been to an institute, and that they should respond by opening their heads so I could, with new skill, pour the knowledge in. Perhaps they should go to an institute (I almost ended that in -ion) to learn how to learn.

The confusion of opening exercises scarcely put a dent in my enthusiasm for the order about to go into effect. But my carefully brainstormed method to be used the First Sunday After Institute fell flat on its face before the period was under way when one of the boys tripped over the extension cord and pulled the slide projector to the floor with a crash.

Nevertheless, I bravely launched into a review of last Sunday's lesson. It turned out that none of the three who had been present could remember even an irrelevant item about it, except that it came the day after they lost their first football game. For the *coup de grace*, my clever discussion starter started nothing but a big argument about whose gun could shoot the farthest.

By the end of the period I felt a peculiar kinship with the seven sons of Sceva. We had read about them from the Book of Acts. The boys in the class got quite a charge out of one man literally beating the pants off all seven of those fellows.

Their predicament now seemed oddly familiar. The sons of Sceva had been engaged in a very worthwhile task: trying to cast out demons. They knew how to go about it; they had the method. They even knew the right words. The Jesus whom Paul preached was their authority. But for their trouble all they got was a good drubbing.

No doubt they would have agreed that it takes more than correct forms or formulas to accomplish God's work. Maybe I've been so intent on getting the procedures down pat that it has become a mechanical thing. As a result, my students naturally react with an attitude that seems to say, "Maybe Jesus and Paul amounted to something; but how are you related to what they said and did?"

Perhaps the secret is to imitate Paul a little more closely. If I could say with him, "I have been crucified with Christ, it is no longer I who live, but Christ who lives in me," then perhaps Christ could accomplish something without tripping over my big feet.

15. ON YOUR MARKS

"See you next Sunday," I said.

The class just sat there. Who had ever heard of closing a class period in this way?

"That's all for today," I added. "You're dismissed."

They took the hint and left, some looking as though they thought their teacher had forgotten to put on an essential piece of clothing.

They may have been right—not about the clothes, but about something being missing. Perhaps the customary prayer is the best way to close the period.

But I had just gotten tired of—no, it was more than that. To use the Lord's Prayer in such a matter-of-fact way at the close of the hour had come to seem actually sacrilegious. It rarely meant anything to anyone.

The way it usually went, the warning bell would

sound—warning teachers to hurry and wind up the lesson, try to give an assignment—and then get out of the way. At the sound of the bell, my young broncos became instantly alert, eager to be the first out of the room.

To conclude the hour with some semblance of decorum, I would say, "Let's pray the Lord's Prayer." Formulas such as, "Let's repeat—recite—or say the Lord's Prayer," grate on my ear, but they really would have been more fitting in our case.

So the sounds of the prayer would be repeated in the traditional and approved mumbling fashion. All the while the boys would be trying to jockey

for position to get out—occasionally nudging their neighbor, stepping on his foot, or bumping his books out of his arms.

The girls, meanwhile, would be putting on their scarves and mittens, buttoning coats, and picking up their books—while trying to keep their eyes closed. If another class beat us by a petition and a half, it seemed almost painful to have to remain behind.

Of course, I was a part of this too. I would put my mouth on automatic pilot and keep my eyes on the class, wondering whether true prayer would be better served by an interruption to maintain better order. Sometimes I did reach out to tap an offender. In any case, there was little praying on my part.

Such hypocrisy was helpful to no one. So this one Sunday we just omitted the closing prayer. But the shock which made for an orderly dismissal isn't likely to last. And the kids were right; something was missing.

Maybe the students could suggest a proper closing which would allow everyone to have a thoughtful part. But I'm convinced the gap shouldn't be plugged with the Lord's Prayer, except on rare occasions, and then only with some kind of preparation. That marvelous prayer is too good to serve only as a starter's signal. It gets entirely too many vain repetitions on a Sunday morning as it is.

16. OPENING SEASON

It's hard to see why there might be resistance to attempts to do away with opening exercises. The time-honored practice of beginning the Sunday school session with a catch-all period of singing ("Let's make it loud!"), reading, and miscellaneous religiosity can cover a multitude of sins.

For instance, if you are one of those who have a problem getting out of bed early enough to get to Sunday school on time, opening exercises can save the day. This procedure can keep members of your class somewhat profitably occupied until you arrive. You can slip in quietly and stand at the rear of the hall as though you had been appointed monitor for the day or something. If you have separate classrooms, you can go directly there and be ahead of time for once.

The same benefit applies to students, too, though not quite to the same degree. At least if they come late they haven't really missed anything. And if too many are late, you can just keep on singing hymns until a respectable enough number shows up to merit holding classes.

It's especially handy to have this extra time nowadays when there is so much emphasis on using equipment and varying methods. While the rest of the Sunday school is opening exercises, you can be opening doors and cupboards to find maps, visual aids, crayons, scissors, paper, or anything else you may need for class.

The longer the opening period the better, of course. Sometimes it may take 20 minutes to find a chalkboard, especially if you have to locate chalk and eraser too. And of course, the longer the opening, the shorter the remaining time for which you are responsible.

It's more convenient if you can do all this getting ready in a separate classroom while all students are assembled elsewhere. But if you must rummage in the back of the assembly room, you probably won't disturb too many people if they are singing good and loud, even if you should knock over the projection screen or drop an armful of commentaries. Such active preparations might even impress some students and fellow teachers.

If you are particularly alert—unlikely as that may be at such an hour on Sunday—you may even be able to look at your lesson for the first time after arriving at the church and still locate something in the supply shelves that will fit in reasonably well.

Obviously, to change opening exercises to a worship period, particularly by departments, would cramp one's style in these practical activities. It might be difficult to make class preparations while worshiping with others. It might even require getting there on time and doing your class preparation beforehand.

17. YOO HOO, ROXANNE

"This year it's not going to be a program! We're going to present a Christmas service." The superintendent was emphatic in putting across this idea at the teachers' meeting.

The change met with general approval. Someone agreed, "Yes, the programs are too much work."

But this attitude was quickly squelched. "It's not the work I'm objecting to," Harry emphasized. "In fact, this may mean more work."

"How will people feel who are used to coming to the Sunday school Christmas programs to be entertained?"

"We'll have to let them know of our plans beforehand."

"And after all," chimed in Mrs. Johnson, "we aren't here to entertain or put on programs. We have a Sunday school to tell people about Jesus, and that should be the purpose of our Christmas program too."

So we began to prepare. It was easy enough to find a suitable service the children could present. Every teacher took special pains to explain to his class that we were going to have a service. When we gave the reasons for the change, the children accepted it as proper, as children will. They were quite willing to tell of their love for Jesus without making it a performance. All our publicity emphasized that this was to be a worship service.

The day of the service came. It was apparent from the time people began to arrive that some hadn't gotten the word. There was a great deal of noisy talking back and forth.

The service was to begin with a prayer by a group of the younger pupils. They had been cautioned not to wave at anyone—and they didn't. But their parents did! One after another, parents waved at their bewildered offspring; a couple stood up to catch a boy's attention; someone whispered loudly, "Roxanne." This, naturally, made a few of the children wave back, and most of them forgot why they were there or how the prayer began.

But with some prompting they began the prayer, although not quite in the worshipful attitude they had had at the beginning. Then a couple of proud papas stood up and took flash pictures. The prayer dribbled off into blank stares and only the prompter finished it.

The next item was a song. When it was over someone began clapping. With remarkable restraint the superintendent got to his feet and announced that this was supposed to be a worship service and would they please refrain from applauding.

So they didn't do it again. But it was too late. Because some people were present who had not come to worship, the atmosphere was spoiled, and no one else could really worship either.

Next year maybe we shouldn't allow parents to come.

18. MAN ABOARD

"What does the board of education do?" Melvin asked one night after our teachers' meeting.

"Oh, you know," Bill answered—"hires the superintendent, signs contracts with teachers, gets taxes raised, spends money . . . "

"No, not that board," Melvin objected. "The one here at church."

"I didn't know there was one," said Bill.

"There must be," Melvin declared. "I was elected to it."

"When did this happen?" I asked.

"Oh, that's right," said George. "The annual meeting was last week. I forgot all about it. Hope I wasn't elected to anything."

"How did you happen to be elected?" Bill asked Melvin. "Weren't you there to defend yourself?"

"As a matter of fact, I wasn't," the new board member admitted. "I might not have known about it yet except the pastor happened to meet me on the street and he congratulated me."

"Why didn't you ask him what you're supposed to do?" I asked.

"I didn't want to let on to him that I was so ignorant. He said we would be having an organizational meeting one of these days. It sounded as though we're in charge of the educational program of the congregation."

"I thought the pastor was in charge," George said.

"Well, I don't suppose he can do everything," Melvin answered.

"After all," Bill observed, "he doesn't even get to Sunday school—he's usually preaching then."

"But we do have a superintendent," George pointed out. "Can't he take charge?"

"Someone has to get him to take the job," I observed.

"Maybe the board has some of the same duties as the board at the public school that Bill began talking about," George suggested.

"What do you mean?" Melvin asked.

"Get a superintendent, recruit other teachers, see that equipment and property are adequate and are taken care of."

"Seems to me someone from a board did sign our calls to be teachers," George recalled.

"How about the taxes?" Melvin asked.

"I can see how it would help if someone could talk intelligently about Sunday school needs at the annual meeting," Bill commented. "And there ought to be someone to make recommendations and authorize expenses."

"I thought the women always looked after this," George said.

"Pastor said he was glad to get a man on the board finally," Melvin said.

"Yeah, I suppose he does get to feel sort of out-numbered at times," I concluded.

"You'd think if a board did all these things we'd hear about it," Bill mused.

"Well, how often do you attend an annual meeting? Anyway, now that you're on the board, Melvin, we'll all expect to hear what you are doing."

"Maybe we'll even come to the annual meeting next year to give you a vote of thanks."

19. UNDER WRAPS

As a general rule, the less one says about women's hats the safer it is.

But one day at home I overheard my children playing Sunday school. "I'll be Mrs. Jensen," volunteered next-door Susie. "Let's see, what can I wear for a hat?" Her solution was a unique creation: a lazy Susan with streamers of purple and green crepe paper.

That is, it seemed unique until the next Sunday. I couldn't resist looking for Mrs. Jensen and her hat. Wow! That veil could have hidden Moses or Paul or anyone! She must be a whale of a teacher if she can divert the attention of her pupils to what she says rather than to what she wears.

In spite of myself I began looking for other hats. Most of the women teachers were wearing them, but in reasonably good taste. Other items of apparel, however, caught the eye just as insistently. Mrs.

Savage's earrings would have done justice to Long John Silver. Each time she moved, eight little heads turned to watch the swinging action as if pulled by a string.

And the little girls in Sadie Olson's class just couldn't keep their eyes, and sometimes their hands, away from the frills and ruffles on their teacher's dress.

Most of the teachers were wearing coats; so were most of the students. I had never noticed this before, but assumed that they made use of the coat-racks that are provided. Our room can scarcely be called chilly.

This observation led me to become an amateur psychologist the next Sunday. "Sort of warm in here, isn't it?" I observed after the class had gathered, although the temperature was no different from usual.

"Yes," was the response.

"Why don't you hang up your wraps?"

They did.

My analysis of the experiment may have been prejudiced, but it did seem that Tom wasn't quite as fidgety as usual. Maybe his neck didn't itch when there wasn't a wool scarf next to it. Jack didn't have his usual supply of playthings since without his jacket he had only half as many pockets to explore.

It was easier to wrap things up too, since Kristi

wasn't perched on the edge of her chair throughout the last ten minutes, waiting for the bell to ring. She had to wait to get her coat on before dashing out. And not one of the girls was putting on a scarf or buttoning her coat during the closing prayer.

20. GOD IS A GUEST

Last Sunday our pastor visited Sunday school. It was the First Sunday in Lent, so our superintendent had asked him to be present at the opening exercises (if you'll pardon the expression) to explain what Lent was all about. He decided to do this by wearing his clerical vestments and explaining why he wore these garments in church and why some of the colors were changed at certain times of the year.

The children were quite impressed. Especially one pre-schooler. She could hardly wait to find her mother after Sunday school to exclaim to her, "God came to Sunday school today!"

This brought a good laugh when it was explained. But after about 30 seconds it began to disturb me. Was there actually a member of our congregation, even though she was quite young, who did not know who our pastor was? How could that happen?

Perhaps it wasn't so strange. After all, if the pastor came to our house, we would probably shush the children out of doors or into the basement—just like the disciples of old.

Besides that, there aren't very many pre-schoolers who come to worship services in our congregation, so they don't have a chance to find out there who the pastor is. And the pastor may act pretty much as I do in a group that includes children—which means to talk to the big folks and forget about the little ones.

On the other hand, the little girl's conclusion about the morning's experience may not have been out of order at all. Is it stretching things to say that God does come to visit us in the person of the minister of the Word? For that matter, the Apostle Paul seems to suggest that Christ should be coming to visit in the person of the teacher of the Word —if I'm doing my job.

And the fact that God is concerned enough about us to want to visit us, by whatever means, should be an occasion for excitement to people of any age.

Even so, there is an uncomfortable question.

In all of our fussing about organizing and running a church school in the proper way—with the myriad of details calling for attention: books, papers, records, pins, envelopes, chairs, coat-racks, and all the rest, necessary as these things are—is it

possible that God's visits to our Sunday school are
as rare as the little girl seemed to think?

21. WHAT DID YOU DO? NOTHING.

A Sunday school teacher sometimes forgets that he is responsible for some other children who go to Sunday school—his own. My subconscious—or perhaps it's the old Adam—tries to persuade me that after all the effort I put into teaching someone else's kids, someone else should be responsible for teaching mine. As a result, my children's teachers probably have the same complaint that I do: "Why won't the parents do something to help?"

At any rate, my conscience got the upper hand last Sunday long enough for me to ask Junior, "What did you do in Sunday school today?"

"Oh, nothing."

We've had this kind of conversation before, so I persisted. "Did you bring anything home?"

"Yeah." After some burrowing under the Sunday paper, he produced an outline picture of a small boy giving his sister a ride in a wagon. Before he told me, I guessed that he had colored it.

"And what's this picture about?"

He shrugged his shoulders. "I don't know."

"Didn't the teacher say anything about it?"

"Sure. She said to color it and keep quiet."

I wasn't ready to give up yet. "Didn't you have a story?"

"I guess so."

"What was it about?"

At last he was sure of an answer: "God!"

"Did you learn a Bible verse?" I asked.

"Sure." He quickly added, "But I can't remember it."

"Let's look at your book," I suggested helpfully. "Maybe you can remember it when you see it again."

This involved a major effort. Upon Junior's return from Sunday school, the book had been immediately outranked by the comics. Its whereabouts had been further obscured by the search for his handwork.

When we finally found it, it was even more of a problem to decide which lesson had been gone over in class. The lessons in the back of the book, at least those with big pictures, seemed as familiar to him as the first ones. All the stories and memory verses seemed equally, though vaguely, remembered.

By checking the calendar we finally picked a lesson. And sure enough, Junior could repeat the Bible verse and he knew most of the story.

Doubtless there is a moral in this for me as a parent. There may be one for me as a teacher too. Would my class members fare any better in a post-session exam? Or have I neglected to be concerned about what they remember after the period is over?

I hope no one asks me tomorrow what our lesson was about.

22. PIN-UPS

Tomorrow is award day. All the students in Sunday school who have been present every Sunday this year (they are allowed to be sick twice, if they bring a written excuse) will receive a pin or bar.

It will go somewhat like this.

Genevieve, who will add a fifth rung to her ladder, will be in her glory. Roger, who has been going to Sunday school just as long and appears to be profiting from it much more, will get his first-year pin. Arnold probably won't be present, because he missed one Sunday again this year.

Mabel will complain, as she has been doing for some time, because the pin system we use is different from the one they used in the town she came from, and she had to start all over. Jimmy will come up crying after the service because he didn't get a pin. And sure enough, investigation will show that he had earned a pin—but there wasn't one left for him.

Still, on the whole it will be a rather happy event. It's the day after the awards have been made that I dread.

First of all, Mrs. Thompsen will call up to ask why her Jane didn't get a pin. After all, she's been a member of the congregation all her life. And that dreadful Nellie Brown, who is not even a member, gets awards every year!

Then Jim Jacobs will collar me on the street and ask why his boy was passed up. And I'll say, "Because he was absent without an excuse."

Jim will say, "Your records must be wrong. If he missed, he was sick." And maybe he's right; but how to prove it now?

After the complaints die down a bit, we can begin the fun of trying to keep records straight for another year—reminding pupils to bring excuses—wondering whether to relax the rules just this once and accept an oral alibi.

And what does it all accomplish? Some say it impresses on the children that what counts in Sunday school is being present—rather than learning about God or having your life changed. It might even suggest to some that we can please God, or at least the church, by following certain rules.

On the other hand, if we believe God's Word is his power to salvation, it surely is worth the fuss to get children to be where they can hear it. After all, we don't stop giving out food at city missions just because most of the patrons come only for the food.

Is there a better way of encouraging attendance?

23. BEYOND THE CALL
OF DUTY

"Didn't the pastor say something about this last week?" I asked. Another teacher had just complained that she couldn't explain a parable to her class.

"When?"

"In the sermon."

"Oh—I wouldn't know."

"I thought you were here last Sunday," I observed innocently.

"I was. At Sunday school, not church."

"Guess I always think of the two as going together."

"Not me. I figure I've done my share by being in Sunday school. Nobody's got any right to expect me to spend another hour sitting through the church service."

"Nobody but God, maybe."

"Anyway," she barged on, "I have to take my children home after Sunday school. What would they do that hour if I were in church?"

"It's hard to say. Mine go to church with me."

"You make them sit through another hour at church? That's not being very considerate of active children."

"Oh, I don't really make them do it. In our family we just all accept it as the thing to do. As far as that goes, I don't really make them sit through a two-hour TV program or movie, either; but they often manage to stick it out all alone."

"But that's something they like."

"Why is going to church such a burden to you? I don't see how you get along without it—or why you'd want to."

"What do you get out of it?"

"First of all, it's an opportunity to worship God."

"You can worship God just as well out in nature."

"Maybe. But I don't find myself, or anyone else, doing it very often. Besides, I need the sermon and the liturgy."

"What good does it do you? Are you any better afterwards?"

"In a way it's like doing laundry. I have my shirts washed even though it never lasts—they always get dirty again. Anyway, there's something about being with other believers and worshiping God together.

73

I gain something from them; and I presume my presence may contribute to others."

"Well, maybe it's okay for you. But Sunday school is enough for me. I get all worn out. It seems too hard to convince the kids that they ought to come."

I wonder if she ever found out the meaning of that parable.

24. EENIE, MEENIE...

"How can you tell God's will for you?" was the question before the class.

Howard had the answer: "Just open the Bible, point to a verse, and you'll find what God wants you to do," he confidently announced.

"Oh yeah, I've done that," agreed Joe.

"So have I," added Norbert. "It doesn't work."

Those who hadn't tried the system took sides for or against it in order to get in on the argument.

"Let's try it," I suggested. "Can you think of a question you'd like to have settled?"

"Whether or not to go to Sunday school next Sunday," suggested Howard.

"You don't need a Bible for that!" was the disgusted rejoinder from Norbert.

"How about if you should go out for basketball?" suggested someone.

This seemed an acceptable problem. "Now just open the Bible," directed Howard.

"Try just a little past the middle," said another exponent of the system. "There are lots of good verses in Proverbs."

But I missed, and we landed in Ezekiel. "Now what?" I asked.

"Close your eyes and point to a verse."

I read the result: "And in the vestibule of the gate were two tables on either side, on which the burnt offering and the sin offering and the guilt offering were to be slaughtered."

"Well, what do you think God's will is?" I asked, looking around at a circle of puzzled looks and wrinkled noses.

Silence. Then Herbert said, "Maybe it means if you go out for basketball you'll be slaughtered." This met with loud and unanimous disapproval.

"I don't think it tells you anything about playing basketball," declared Nellie slowly. The class agreed.

"Do you think there might be any danger in using this system?" I asked. "Any chance you might get some really poor advice?"

"Naw, it's just a waste of time," snorted Norbert.

"What if your first passage turned out to be Matthew 27:5?" There was a scurried hunt for the passage, followed by a low whistle. "Then," I continued, "if that didn't please you, what if you turned next to Luke 10:37?"

"I'm not going to use this system," said Kristi with conviction.

We eventually concluded that although the Bible is the place to look to learn God's will, it's somewhat dangerous to treat it like magic.

25. JUNIOR KNOWS BEST

"Why not ask the youngsters who have just been confirmed to teach?"

This suggestion came from one of our ladies who found all of her excuses for not teaching falling apart. "After all, they have just studied all these things, and they know more about it than we who were confirmed—well, quite a few years ago now," she concluded with a coy flourish.

"Are you bragging or complaining?"

"What do you mean?"

"Are you bragging or complaining that you don't know as much about your faith as you once did?" I explained.

She seemed to get almost embarrassed. But she was equal to the situation. "Neither. Just being realistic. I guess the church could stand to be realistic now and then, couldn't it?"

She was pleased when I indicated agreement. But

I went on. "You know, you may have something. It might even save us some tax money."

"How?"

"Well, would you say that high school students who have just studied, oh, geometry, or American history, may know more about the subject than most adults?"

"Of course."

"Then why not have them teach those subjects to the people in the class below them. Think of the saving if we didn't have to pay teachers."

Before she could say anything, I went on. "Or take another practical matter. Mrs. Schultz, how much do you know about how a car operates?"

"Cars? Not very much, I'll admit. I can drive one, that's about all."

"How about your son in the ninth grade?"

"Oh, he knows all about them. He reads all those magazines, fusses with motors—he just can't wait until he can get a driver's license."

"Since he apparently knows so much more about it," I observed, "wouldn't it be more realistic for him to drive, rather than you?"

"But there's more to driving than just knowing about engines!" she protested.

"Is there more to driving than there is to the Christian faith?"

"Well . . ." she began. But it dried up.

"But really, something else you said bothers me. If it's normal for an adult to forget all he's taught, why bother teaching him Christianity in the first place?"

She still isn't teaching.

26. GHOSTS AND GOD

"What day is next Monday?" I asked the class.

That was easy. They answered immediately with joyful accord, "Halloween!"

"Well, I guess that's true," I admitted. "But can anyone think of another special name for the day?"

Silence—tinged with an attitude that anything else it might possibly be couldn't hold a candle to Halloween in importance.

"Something that's important to us in the church," I hinted.

"Easter?" was a hesitant venture, immediately hooted down.

"Something to do with the Holy Ghost?" guessed an imaginative soul. This brought an appreciative murmur.

"Did you ever hear of a man called Luther?" I asked after a long silence.

"Yes!" they chorused. The mystery was beginning to intrigue them.

"It's his birthday," shouted one of the boys.

"No, but you're getting warm," I said. "Monday is Reformation Day. Ever hear of that?"

A few cautious nods.

"On October 31, way back in 1517," I said, launching into what the teaching-methods books call a one-minute lecture, "Martin Luther posted a notice on a church door. It said he disagreed with some things going on in the church. Do you know what happened as a result?"

"I know," said Howard. "I saw the movie. He got kicked out of the church."

"That did happen after awhile," I agreed. "Did anything good result?"

"I think we got the Bible," replied Norbert.

"At least more people got to know what it said," I nodded.

"Didn't they have to pay a priest to have their sins forgiven before that?" asked Joe.

"And now God does it for free," affirmed Nellie.

"If we can trace such things to October 31, 1517," I asked them, "don't you think it is a day worth remembering?"

"Sure. It's as important as Christmas," Joe responded.

"Not quite, Joe," I said. "Luther didn't really do anything—God had already done everything on Christmas and Easter and Pentecost. Luther just rediscovered what God had done and told others."

"If it's so important, why don't we celebrate it?" Norbert wanted to know.

"Yeah, you never hear of anything but Halloween."

Looks as though we've been hiding our light under a jack-o'-lantern.

27. DEAD RESPECT

When I was a boy the chancel was a holy place —though we didn't know that was its name. You just never went near the altar except on festival Sundays when everybody had to march around it with their offerings. As for going inside the altar rail, well, you remember what happened to Aaron's sons, or that fellow who touched the Ark of the Covenant!

It seemed almost sacrilegious for the women to go inside the altar railing to get the altar candles for cleaning. And I remember what a feeling of adventure it gave to walk up the steps and across the carpet of the chancel to the side room.

Imagine the shock, then, to find some children playing hide-and-seek around the altar. To them it was just like any other room—with rather odd furniture.

Perhaps in our day we didn't have exactly the

right attitude. But you can say this much for it: It didn't hinder us from recognizing that sin is serious, or that there is a great difference between God and us, best acknowledged by such words as *awe*.

This attitude showed up in many ways. For example, there was a time when people dressed up only on Sundays; it was a mark of respect for God. Even the Saturday night bath was a part of this. Now, because of changing economics and customs, many people are dressed up every day, and the chances are that they will wear informal clothes most of Sunday.

To be sure, we still teach the children that they should *fear* God. But you're probably bothered as much as I am as to how we should explain that. I usually end up by talking about reverence.

However, reverence seems to be the sort of thing that is learned mostly by observation or imitation. Perhaps children don't have much of an example to follow.

It is understandably difficult to learn to revere a God who is regarded as a sort of doctor, or repair man, or banker—handy to have on call when needed —or even as a magician for those who know the right words. Or as a pal—the Old Man upstairs. A nameless Someone doesn't garner too much respect either.

Students can tell whether the reverence we display is genuine. They probably also take note of what we really revere most. For example, we have great respect for certain people who have been safely dead for a respectable length of time. We act reverently around places where such people once lived and died.

But we don't always show equal reverence for God.

28. BE HAPPY OR ELSE!

"You shouldn't always use the same method in teaching."

"Amen!" I said with conviction—silently, of course.

The speaker droned on. "How can you expect to hold the interest of a group of youngsters, much less have them really learn anything if you just stand up in front of them and drone away?"

Half-heartedly I tried to muffle a yawn as I looked around at the group of teachers who had braved the nice weather to attend our monthly teachers' meeting. Several full-length eyelids were in view.

Now we'll at least get a chance to stretch, I thought, when I heard the statement, "Even adults get tired of the same thing all the time. Use variety in your presentations."

He went right on. "Visual aids should not be

overlooked." Then he proceeded to lecture on these means of teaching.

Finally the hour was over. The leader came over to me. "I really appreciate your coming so faithfully to these teachers' meetings. It's a shame so few attend. I wish I knew what to do about it."

Should I tell him?

He went on. "It's the same way at Bible study. Just a few come."

Oh yes, the Bible study class. I had attended a few times. The instructor used to keep saying something like this: "You must get into the Word yourself before it can really benefit you as it should." Then he would use the rest of the period to lecture us on what we would learn if we would read the Bible.

Suddenly my own class came to mind. I could hear myself saying, "You must memorize this." But my book was open in front of me so I could tell whether or not they had done it.

Or I have growled, "A Christian should be happy."

Again I have demanded, "Why don't you kids bring your Bibles to Sunday school?"—while finding the place for myself in a copy from the supply shelf.

"Bring your friends to Sunday school," I've told them. But have I ever invited anyone? I impress on them the need for daily prayer and Bible study; but frankly I hope they are more faithful than I.

Though I emphasize the importance of love and forgiveness, it seems to be less important after they have played a prank on me.

Sometimes I have scolded them for not worshiping during the opening service. I knew they weren't because I was standing guard at the back of the room.

"Don't do as I do; do as I say," a rather unambitious teacher once told his class. But we never followed that advice.

Students never do.

29. "I'VE HAD IT"

"Me go to Sunday school?" Louis asked the question as if my senses had just left on furlough.

Yes, I admitted that was what I had been leading up to.

"But I've been confirmed," was the confident reply, "—25 years ago."

"A fine beginning, I'm sure," I said in my most fatherly tone. "Now isn't it time to build on that foundation—that is, if the foundation is still standing."

"But I've had all that," he protested, not sure whether he should be exasperated at the humiliating implication of my statement or puzzled by my thick-skulled failure to accept the obvious.

"You've had all what?"

"You know, the Ten Commandments, Bible history—the usual course."

"You know it, huh? Good. Then you can take

over my class while I join the adult Bible class to brush up on a few things."

"Ah—I may not know it that well, I suppose," he hastily mumbled. "But Sunday school is for kids."

"Have you ever heard anyone say that except someone who doesn't want to go? Grandpa Olson is in his second childhood, then, since he attends Bible class?"

"No," he admitted. "But he probably has nothing else to do."

"And during that hour you . . . ?"

"Aw, a fellow has to catch up on sleep sometime. Really, I'm not as much of a heathen as you're trying to make me out to be. I'm a pretty good church member; I'm in favor of all they do. And

I did go to Sunday school—for years. It's just that it's always the same old stuff."

"You think the adult class spends all their time memorizing the Ten Commandments? If that were true you might have a point. If you thought beef always came strained in baby food jars you might not react with enthusiasm to an invitation to a steak fry."

Some folks never got more than Pablum in religious education. Perhaps that's all they were offered; or maybe they quit before they were ready for the steak. As a result they don't know there is something you can sink your teeth into in Sunday school.

Please pass the steak.

30. HALF RECIPE

Teaching is something like baking. It helps to have a recipe to follow, especially for some of us newer teachers. But the directions need to be rather exact. Even my wife has trouble with recipes in old church cookbooks that say, "Fill a pan with potatoes," or "Take the butter that's left over from dinner."

Fortunately, both cookbooks and teaching materials have improved and now usually provide very helpful directions. However, they still aren't foolproof.

For example, my wife once asked me to finish baking some biscuits while she dashed off to a meeting at church. I looked at the open cookbook, discovered that the recipe should make 48 biscuits, and proceeded to divide the dough into that many piles. What I did not know was that my wife had made only half a recipe!

Sometimes I've done just about the same thing in teaching. The chapter for the day may have six sub-topics. Our period is 30 minutes long. It's not hard to figure out that that means about five minutes for each subject. The result can be about as palatable as marble-sized biscuits. I'm learning that it's better to divide the lesson into fewer pieces which will be more interesting and valuable to the students—even if it means omitting some material, or bringing it in with another lesson, or dealing with it outside of class. After all, my wife doesn't haul everything out of the cupboards for every meal!

At least I'm not the only amateur—even in cooking. I heard of a lady who used a recipe which indicated it should provide 36 cookies. So when she had put 36 cookies on her baking sheet, she threw the rest of the dough away.

I was reminded of her the other Sunday when one of the members of my class asked a question. It was relevant, but it wasn't included in my lesson plan for the day. I looked at my watch, and at the material in the chapter still to be covered, and decided we couldn't take time for the question. By that decision I threw away whatever interest remained in at least some of the students. We would have accomplished much more if I had taken part of another period to make use of this extra "dough," even if it meant omitting something else.

At least our dog liked the biscuits.

31. JUDGED

Some time ago I was guilty of the sin of judging. It wasn't the first time, by any means; nor, unfortunately, the last. But this particular instance will live long in my memory because of the way it backfired.

A couple of our Sunday school teachers had been teaching some things, and at times exhibiting an attitude, that seemed to me to be inconsistent with the Christian faith. Sad to say, I let someone know my verdict.

Naturally, the word eventually got around to the parties concerned, probably somewhat embellished. When they heard about it, the two teachers reacted in rather different ways.

The first came flying at me like a wounded she-bear shot out of a cannon. "What do you mean by saying I'm not a Christian?" was her outraged greeting.

Even before the smile of recognition had faded from my face, she let me have it with the other barrel.

"I'll have you know I'm every bit as good a Christian as you are. Just because I'm not willing to hog-tie my brain with the outmoded superstitions of the last century and don't act or speak in your holy manner doesn't mean that I'm not as good as you are. At least I don't go around damning everyone who doesn't behave the way I think they ought to. There's something about that in the Bible, too, it seems to me. I'll thank you to keep your judgments to yourself until somebody elects you judge!"

No one had ever called me holy before. But it didn't seem too appropriate to express my gratitude at the compliment just at that moment. And before anything else came into my mind, she had turned on her heel and stamped away.

Scarcely had I gotten back my wind before I saw the second wronged teacher looming over the horizon. I cringed before the anticipated onslaught. But to my grateful surprise, the conversation opened quietly, something like this:

"I'm sorry that I offended you and caused you to doubt my Christian faith. I'm afraid my witness for Christ isn't very effective, is it? I'm always doing something to embarrass him. Actually it didn't occur to me that I might be doing something contrary to God's will. But I'm sorry if I did. I hope I can learn to be a better witness in my life."

You can readily imagine that I felt like two cents —after taxes.

I'll have to admit that this incident didn't cure me of the sin of judging. In fact, I made another judgment right then and there. But at least I was convinced that I had made a wrong judgment in the case of at least one of the two aforementioned persons.

Perhaps you can guess which one.

32. LOST AND FOUND

"I couldn't find my book."

This, obviously, was an ironclad alibi for not knowing the lesson. But it had been used so many times that I felt something should be done about it.

"When did you discover it was missing?"

"This morning."

"How long had it been lost?"

"I don't know."

"Did you have it last Sunday?"

"I can't remember."

"Well, I can—and you didn't." Turning to the class I said, "It looks like this fellow needs some help."

"Has he looked in the church kitchen?" Joe asked eagerly. "That's where I found my book when it was lost."

"The pastor returned mine to me once," Kristi added helpfully.

"Those are possibilities if you lose the book at church," I agreed. "But what if it happens at home?"

"Maybe it got carted out with the Sunday paper," Tom suggested.

"Have you looked under the TV?" asked Carolyn.

"Maybe your kid sister took it to play school with," was Jack's contribution.

We didn't seem to be approaching a remedy. So I asked, "How do the rest of you keep from losing your books?" Then I realized that I was probably addressing only one or two of them.

"My mother makes me keep it in the same spot on the bookshelf as soon as I come home," Norbert volunteered.

"I keep mine on a table in my room," Nellie said.

"I can never find mine," Jane admitted. "But usually Mom can find it Sunday morning." So that's why she comes tardy and unprepared.

"What can we do about a person who comes to class without a book?"

"Make him look on with a girl," someone suggested.

"Have an extra book here for him to use," was Howard's solution.

"Make him do next Sunday's lesson before he leaves," said Kristi.

"Tie the book around his neck when he leaves Sunday school," said Joe.

Suddenly Jack said, "Hey, I've got your book, Howard!"

"You must have had it all the time," Howard reproved him.

"Now I wonder where mine is," Jack lamented.

33. GOD BLESS EVERYTHING

"God bless everybody. Amen."

I don't remember what bright lad first got the idea for this prayer. It surely made easy work of the sentence prayer period. The other members of the class were quick to see the thought-conserving potential of this formula.

"God bless our country."

"God bless the church."

"God bless the missionaries."

Maybe I should have been happy about such ready participation in prayer. But it didn't quite sound like real prayer. And I was convinced the class members were not learning good prayer habits by such a practice.

Finally I asked, "What do you mean by 'bless'?" There was a lengthy silence.

"It's something they say in the Bible and in church," was the first attempt at an answer.

"It means something good," added someone else.

If they had asked me, I might not have been able to add much to their definitions. But the man who wrote, "Bless the Lord . . . all that is within me, bless his holy name," must have had something rather more dynamic and demanding in mind.

Nevertheless, if the youngsters, by using the word "bless," meant to ask God to do something good for a person, perhaps that is enough. But to further dilute it by seeking this rather vague good for no one in particular makes it pretty weak—like trying to help all the people in India by throwing a handful of pennies in the direction of their country.

"Whom were you thinking about in these prayers?" I asked the class.

"Nobody in particular," was the honest reply.

The Bible says to pray for all men, but I doubt that Paul would have let us by with a "God bless all men. Amen."

Once I had a teacher with a remarkable ability to expose the glib-tongued bluffer who hadn't read the assignment but could give a smooth recitation of fine-sounding, if meaningless, generalities. Her cold interruption, "Be specific," never failed to expose the loafer.

It's good advice for prayer too.

34. REMEMBER THE MEMBERS

"When I'm a member of the church, I'm going to be an usher," announced Howard in a pre-class discussion I happened to overhear.

Howard came from a very active family in our church. So I interrupted, "Aren't you baptized, Howard?"

"Sure," he said.

"Doesn't that make you a member?"

"I don't know," he shrugged. "But you aren't really a member till you're grown up."

The others seemed to agree. They just didn't feel that they were a part of the church yet, although all of them were listed on the church membership roll.

They may have good reason for their attitude. When youngsters their age or younger come to services, the usher often views them with suspicion. He doesn't give them a bulletin, and at best tries to ignore them as much as possible. Too often the pastor forgets to appeal to their understanding or experience in what he says. No wonder they begin to feel that church isn't for them.

Undoubtedly it is unintentional, but many people today reflect the attitude of the disciples who tried to keep the children from Jesus.

Others do it intentionally. Educators even write articles referring to the small children who don't belong in church. In effect, some of them are telling us, "Don't let a child experience grown-up religion; don't include him too often." And so the child remains a child.

This can have at least two effects. For one thing, Sunday school becomes all there is to church as far as the child is concerned. The idea seems to be: Sunday school for children, church for grownups. When the children grow up, they theoretically will exchange the Sunday school for the church. But one whose only experience with church has been Sunday school may not easily adjust to church—or he may not even want to try.

In the second place, the child assumes Sunday school is not for adults, so when he grows up he ignores this opportunity for continued instruction, so vital for spiritual growth.

A pastor once said, "It may be comfortable not to have children in church, but is it the church?"

35. WHAT'S A DEARIE?

"I hear the board of education is thinking about getting a DRE," observed Dick one night after teachers' meeting.

"What's a 'dearie'?" asked George.

"A D.R.E.—director of religious education," spelled out Dick.

"I'm all for that," exclaimed George. "I'll be glad to turn over my duties to someone else."

"What duties are you going to turn over?" I asked.

"Why, teaching Sunday school," he replied.

"You expect us to hire a director of religious education simply to let you out of a job?" John asked.

"Well, I suppose she'd have other things to do," was his response. "Released time classes, secretarial work, the parish paper, straightening up around the building—I'm sure we could find plenty to keep her busy."

"You don't want a DRE. You want a platoon of slaves with master's degrees," observed Dick.

"If she's going to teach fifth grade for you, how about the rest of us?" asked John. "Maybe we'd like help, too."

"Yeah. She can't teach all the grades, and it would hardly be fair to take just one," I pointed out.

"I guess she'd have to be superintendent then," George mused.

"Wonder if Harry would like to give up his job?" John asked.

"We had a DRE in the congregation I came from," Dick said. "She didn't take anyone's job —not even the superintendent's."

"What's the use of getting someone then?" asked George.

"She just made the rest of us more effective," Dick said. "She gave the superintendent a lot of help, but didn't take over. At the teachers' meetings she got a chance to tell us about new books and techniques. She ran a pre-service training course for new teachers. It really did us all a lot of good. Even the board of education. They seemed to get more done, though she didn't take over their job, either."

As an afterthought he added, "In our case she taught an adult class too, when we couldn't get a teacher. Added interest made it necessary to start more classes."

"You think it's good, I take it," John observed.

"By all means," Dick agreed.

"Say, why do you always say 'her'?" I asked.

"What do you expect from a bachelor?" Dick laughed.

"You mean men do this work, too?" George asked in surprise.

"Why not," John concluded. "It sounds like a man-sized job."

For anyone who does all that, maybe "dearie" is the right title.

THE AUTHOR

Rolf E. Aaseng is associate editor of *The Lutheran Standard,* official publication of The American Lutheran Church. Along with his editorial duties, he has written a well-received column entitled "Lifelines." This is a series of interpretations of the books of the Bible. Previously, while serving as editor of *The Lutheran Teacher,* he edited teacher training materials.

Mr. Aaseng holds degrees from Concordia College, Moorhead, Minn., Luther Theological Seminary, St. Paul, Minn., and Biblical Seminary, New York. Prior to assuming an editorial post with Augsburg Publishing House, he served as publicity director of the former Evangelical Lutheran Church and was pastor of a church at Park Rapids, Minn.